Grammar, Punctuation & Spelling Activity Book

for ages 8-9

This CGP book is bursting with fun activities to build up children's skills and confidence.

It's ideal for extra practice to reinforce what they're learning in primary school. Enjoy!

Published by CGP

Editors:
Rachel Craig-McFeely, Catherine Heygate, Harry Millican

With thanks to Alison Griffin and Gabrielle Richardson for the proofreading.

With thanks to Jan Greenway for the copyright research.

ISBN: 978 1 78908 523 5

Printed by Elanders Ltd, Newcastle upon Tyne.
Images throughout the book from www.edu-clips.com
Cover design concept by emc design ltd.

Contents

Word types

How It Works

Nouns are naming words. Adjectives are words that describe nouns.

The greedy dog eats quickly.

↑ ↑
adjective   noun

Verbs are doing or being words. Adverbs often describe verbs.

My dog growls loudly.

↑ ↑
verb   adverb

Now Try These

1. Draw lines to match each word with its word type.

 shaggy

 angrily

 kennel

 noun

 adjective

 verb

 adverb

 bird

 naughty

 barked

2. Use four of the words from question 1 to write a sentence.
   Make sure you use a noun, an adjective, a verb and an adverb.

....

....

3. Label the underlined words with their word type.

Sophie <u>absolutely</u> <u>loves</u> reading <u>books</u> about <u>friendly</u> animals.

Dominic <u>said</u> singing has <u>always</u> been his <u>favourite</u> <u>hobby</u>.

4. Use the words in the box to complete the sentences. In the empty boxes, write whether each word is a noun, an adjective, a verb or an adverb.

| shark amazing often walks |

Millie doesn't .... tidy her bedroom.

He normally .... back home after school.

The .... showed off its glistening teeth.

Sadiq said that the film was ....

An Extra Challenge

Some words can be nouns or verbs depending on what sentence they are in.

Here is an example:

We go for a walk.   I walk my dog.
↑   ↑
noun   verb

How many other words can you think of that can be nouns or verbs? Use the picture to help you.

Woof! Can you identify these word types? Woof!

Verbs

How It Works

Verbs change depending on who is doing the action.

I sail.   She sails.

Tenses tell you when things happen.

The pirate sails across the ocean. ← Use the simple present tense for things that happen regularly.

Use the simple past tense for things that happened in the past. → **The pirate sailed across the ocean.**

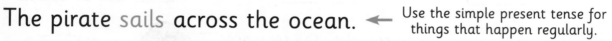

Verbs in the same sentence should usually be in the same tense.

Now Try These

1. Draw lines to show whether these sentences use verbs correctly or incorrectly.

Correct

The pirates counts their treasure.

He fed his parrot a peanut.

I has to walk the plank.

She love exploring desert islands.

Last week, I went to a pirate feast.

You clean the ship with your mop.

Yesterday, he says hello to the captain.

We eat sea biscuits for lunch.

Incorrect

2. There are some mistakes in the tenses in the passage below.
   Can you rewrite the passage without any mistakes?

   Yesterday, it is raining so my dad drives me to school.

   After school finished, I go to the park. I ran around

   and play on the swings until my mum picks me up.

   ....

   ....

   ....

   ....

3. Underline the incorrect verb in each sentence and rewrite it
   correctly. The sentences should be in the simple present tense.

   I is angry with the other pirates.   ➡   ....

   We goes to the treasure island.   ➡   ....

   Lara feel very seasick.   ➡   ....

   They shouts really loudly.   ➡   ....

An Extra Challenge

Tomasz is describing how he buried his treasure on a secret island.

First, I dived off my ship into the sea.

Use the verbs below to continue the description. Make sure you stay in the same tense.

to swim

to run

to see

to dig

Ahoy me hearty! How did it go?
Can you use verbs correctly?

5

Verbs with 'ing'

How It Works

Verbs with 'ing' are used to make the progressive form.

The present progressive form shows an action that is happening now.

She is baking biscuits.

Present tense
form of 'to be'.

The main verb with
'ing' on the end.

The past progressive form shows an action that was happening in the past.

He was kneading the dough.

The past progressive form uses the past tense form of 'to be'.

Now Try These

1. Circle the sentences below that use the progressive form.

You are kind.

She is running.

I was smiling.

They screamed.

They are playing.

I have finished.

He is happy.

We were jumping.

You were speaking.

It is raining.

We replied.

She had gone.

2. Copy the sentences you circled in question 1 into the boxes below to show whether they use the present progressive form or the past progressive form.

Present Progressive	Past Progressive
....	....
....	....
....	....

3. Can you complete each of the sentences below with the past progressive form of a verb from the box?

Jeremy .... pink frosting on his cupcakes.

They .... brownies for the bake sale.

Hiba .... her birthday cake into slices.

We .... the kitchen when my uncle arrived.

I .... happy because my sister had made me a biscuit.

It was a disaster — the icing .... off the cake!

clean	make
cut	put
feel	slide

4. Rewrite the sentences below using the progressive form shown in brackets.

You laugh. ➡ (past) ➡ ....

I skip. ➡ (present) ➡ ....

They paint. ➡ (present) ➡ ....

Ash sings. ➡ (past) ➡ ....

We play. ➡ (present) ➡ ....

An Extra Challenge

Yesterday, Chidi, Ellen and Marta were doing some baking.

Can you use the past progressive form to describe what they were doing?

How would your sentences change if they were doing the baking right now?

Chidi   Ellen   Marta

How is it going? Are you progressively improving?

Verbs with 'have'

How It Works

You can use the present tense of 'have' to talk about things that happened recently.

I have discovered a fossil.

This is the present perfect form.

You can use the past tense of 'have' to talk about things that happened before something else.

I had climbed a tree, so the dinosaur didn't find me.

This is the past perfect form.

The verb after 'have' is usually the same as the simple past tense, but some verbs are different.

The dinosaur has broken it.   We had run away.

not 'has broke'   *not 'had ran'*

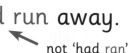

Now Try These

1. Draw lines to show whether these sentences use the present perfect form or the past perfect form.

She had smiled kindly.

He has gone out.

I had hidden the chair.

You have said hello.

Present Perfect Form

Past Perfect Form

We had cooked dinner.

We have begun dancing.

It had torn my coat.

They have swum for hours.

2. Circle the right form of the verb to complete each sentence. In the boxes, write whether each sentence uses the present perfect form or the past perfect form.

Rhys has **rung / rang** the bell very loudly.

It was so cold that the lake had **froze / frozen** .

My friends had **come / came** to stay with us.

Someone has **stole / stolen** the dinosaur tooth.

3. Rewrite this passage using the present perfect form of each verb.

I learned about fossils at school. I decided to go to the museum to learn more and I invited Lila to come too.

....

....

....

....

An Extra Challenge

How many verbs can you think of that are different in the simple past tense and when they're used after 'have'? Use the picture to help you.

Example:
I <u>did</u> it.
I have <u>done</u> it.

Did you roar through these pages? Give yourself a tick.

9

Pronouns

How It Works

Pronouns are words that are used to replace nouns.

Ali **was going to play** the flute,
but she **left** it **at home.**

'She' is a pronoun which replaces the name 'Ali'.

'It' is a pronoun which replaces 'the flute'.

Possessive pronouns show who owns something.

Ali had forgotten her flute, so Sean lent her his.

The possessive pronoun 'his' is used instead of 'Sean's flute'. It shows that the flute belongs to Sean.

Now Try These

1. Circle the words below that are pronouns.

 the   hers    mine   them    Samuel   my

 our   her    Rita    it   your   ours

2. Copy any possessive pronouns you circled in question 1 into the box below.

Possessive Pronouns

3. Rewrite each sentence, replacing the underlined nouns with pronouns.

Clare enjoys playing the drums and <u>Clare</u> plays <u>the drums</u> well.

....

....

Grant and Salem hate maths because <u>Grant and Salem</u> think <u>maths</u> is boring.

....

....

4. Use the pronouns in the box to complete the sentences below.

| him | us | mine | it |

You can't wear those socks because they're ....

My cat dislikes water — .... hates getting wet.

Nadia and I were noisy, so the teacher told .... off.

It was my brother's birthday, so I gave .... a gift.

An Extra Challenge

Answer the questions below using the possessive pronouns in the box.

Lu and Mel

Priya

Liam

| hers | his | theirs |

a) Whose is the guitar?

b) Whose is the harp?

c) Whose is the xylophone?

d) Whose are the cymbals?

e) Whose is the tambourine?

How did <u>you</u> find that?
Are you a pro at pronouns?

Determiners

How It Works

Determiners are small words that go before a noun to tell you more about it.

Articles are the most common type of determiner. 'A', 'an' and 'the' are all articles.

I saw a superhero.

Use 'a' or 'an' for general things.

I saw the superhero.

Use 'the' for specific things.

There are lots of other determiners. Here are a few examples:

I beat that villain. ← This means a specific villain.

You saved some people. ← These could be any people.

I have two hero outfits. ← This determiner shows how many things there are.

They used their powers. ← This determiner shows who owns something.

Now Try These

1. Circle the determiners in each sentence below.

We are a team of four penguin heroes. We use our superpowers for good.

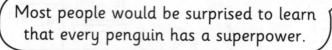

Most people would be surprised to learn that every penguin has a superpower.

My superpower is sliding on my stomach at supersonic speeds — I've used this power to catch many baddies!

Some penguins use their powers for evil deeds, like stealing fish fingers from the supermarket — it's our job to stop them.

2. Circle the right determiner in each sentence below.

Add **some** / **one** spoonful of sugar to the cup of tea.

These / **This** penguin is famous for his dancing skills.

Several / **That** people competed in the unicycle race.

Most / **Every** superheroes keep their identity secret.

3. Use the determiners in the box to complete the sentences below.
   You should only use each determiner once.

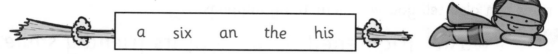

a   six   an   the   his

If I had .... superpower, it would be .... power of flight.

Zack and .... sidekick defeated .... bad guys.

There was .... explosion, but luckily nobody was hurt.

An Extra Challenge

Oh no! Dr Dastardly, the wicked super-villain, has stolen all the determiners from the sentences below. Can you replace all the missing determiners? Try to use as many different ones as possible.

Superheroes used powers to try to defeat baddie.

Determiners were found with help of brave heroes.

Dr Dastardly is evil genius.

Wicked super-villain imprisoned people but prisoner escaped.

How did it go? Is using determiners your superpower?

Prepositions

How It Works

Prepositions tell you where or when something happens.
They are always followed by a noun, a pronoun or a noun phrase.

On Monday, I found a monster **in** my cupboard.

This tells you when
I found the monster.

This tells you where
I found the monster.

Prepositions can also tell you why something happens.

I wasn't frightened **because of** its friendly smile.

This tells you why
I wasn't scared.

Now Try These

1. Circle the words below that are prepositions.

| after | invisible | scary | hiding | spider |

| haunt | beside | until | scream | between |

2. Use the prepositions you circled in question 1 to complete the sentences below.

The witch finally found her hat .... a long search.

Mai couldn't choose .... the pizza and the burger.

"We have .... sunset to cast the spell," whispered Nigel.

Honey promised to stay .... me, but she ran away.

14

3. Underline the preposition in each sentence. Then, draw lines to show whether each preposition tells you where, when or why something happens.

The magician has hidden a rabbit inside his hat.

I was annoyed that people kept talking during the film.

We'll explore the haunted mansion at the weekend.

The vampire dropped a large pumpkin on his toe.

Due to bad weather, the Halloween party was cancelled.

where

when

why

4. Complete the sentences below. Make sure you use a preposition in each one.

Romesh put his cloak ....

They went for a walk ....

Lisa was running ....

An Extra Challenge

Can you describe where each labelled thing is in the picture below?
Try to use a different preposition each time.

Did you find this page scarily good? Or was it just scary?

Noun phrases

How It Works

A phrase is usually a group of words without a verb. A noun phrase is made up of a noun and any words that describe the noun.

the magic wand ⟵ This is a noun phrase.

You can expand noun phrases by adding extra adjectives, prepositions and nouns. This is an expanded noun phrase:

the wizard's new magic wand with a star on top

noun ↑   adjectives ↑   noun ↑   preposition ↑

Now Try These

1. Circle the groups of words below that are noun phrases.

a noble knight

the starry robe

smiling widely

really friendly

flying very quickly

the towering giant

on his head

2. Circle the noun in each underlined noun phrase below.

Neville was surprised when <u>a brightly-coloured unicorn</u> appeared.

<u>The small, angry-looking duck</u> quacked at me from the pond.

I played football on <u>a rather cold, cloudy afternoon</u>.

3. Underline the longest noun phrase in each sentence below.
   The first one has been done for you.

The large green dragon in the living room yawned loudly.

Rob likes to cut the grass with his huge red lawnmower.

Shazia was amazed by the huge castle on top of the hill.

Sarah wrote a long, boring book about the history of paperclips.

4. Rewrite the sentences below, expanding each underlined noun phrase by adding extra words before and after the noun.

The prince ate the sandwich.

....

She ran away from the monster.

....

The queen lives in a palace.

....

An Extra Challenge

Can you come up with a noun phrase to describe each labelled thing in the picture below? Try to include words before and after the nouns.

dwarf

house

ogre

man

wolf

Are noun phrases your fairytale subject? Give yourself a tick.

Planet hopping

Zoobah is trying to get home, but he needs to find enough fuel for his spaceship. Answer each question correctly to work out which planets he should land on to collect fuel. Careful — if you get any questions wrong, he won't be able to reach his home planet.

Start here

1

2

3

A True or false? 'And' is a co-ordinating conjunction.

- True — Move forward two spaces
- False — Move forward one space

4

5

B How many spelling mistakes can you spot in the sentence below? Move forward one space for each mistake you spot.

On a tipical day, Millie bakes three delicious chocolate cakes.

6

C Move forward one space for each determiner you find in the sentence below.

When the alien's rocket crashed, every star went out.

7

13

14

Home

G True or false? A main clause doesn't make sense on its own.

- True — Move forward one space
- False — Move forward two spaces

11

F The sentence below contains some punctuation mistakes. Move forward one space for each mistake you find.

The astronaut's found walking on the Moons' surface hard because there wasnt much gravity.

10

9

E How many pronouns can you spot in the sentence below? Move forward one space for each one.

My cat was playing with his toy.

8

D Which of these words is not an adverb?

- slowly — Move forward two spaces
- well — Move forward one space
- jolly — Move forward three spaces

Adverbials

How It Works

Adverbials are groups of words that act like adverbs.
They describe how, when, where or how often things happen.

The birds flew around the nest. ← This describes where the birds flew.

When an adverbial appears at the start of a sentence, it is usually followed by a comma.

On Saturday, Jack mowed the lawn.

adverbial →   ← comma

Now Try These

1. Write the groups of words that are adverbials in the box below.

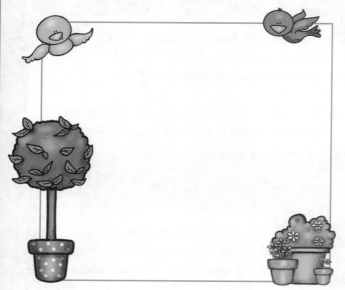

the day is bright

little white flowers

really easily

every weekend

a short walk

a lovely morning

quite regularly

he said hello

in the trees

while it is sunny

2. Underline the adverbial in each sentence.

The children tend the garden very carefully.

The hungry chicks followed Pavel into the house.

He tries to have a healthy lunch every single day.

Before I went into the garden, I put my wellies on.

3. Put a comma in the right place in each sentence below.

In the garden there are lots of colourful flowers.

After waving frantically we finally got Jen's attention.

On special occasions I have ice cream for breakfast.

Tomorrow afternoon we will plant the seeds.

4. Rewrite each sentence with the adverbial at the start.

The frost will melt in the morning.

....

I visited my aunt during the holidays.

....

The dog barks when it is scared.

....

An Extra Challenge

Can you describe what is happening in the picture below?
Try to use an adverbial in each sentence you write.

Do adverbials give you an extra spring in your step? Tick a box.

Clauses

How It Works

Sentences are made up of phrases and clauses.

Ravi did an experiment in the science lab.

A clause has a verb (did) and
someone doing the verb (Ravi).

A phrase doesn't
usually include a verb.

A main clause makes sense on its own. A subordinate clause
gives extra information, but it doesn't make sense on its own.

Vicky raised her hand because she knew the answer.

main clause   subordinate clause

Now Try These

1. Draw lines to show whether each box below contains a phrase or a clause.

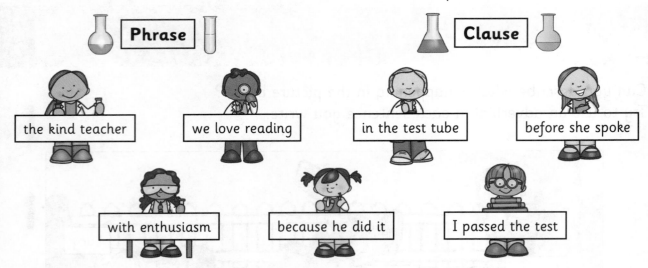

Phrase   **Clause**

the kind teacher   we love reading   in the test tube   before she spoke

with enthusiasm   because he did it   I passed the test

2. Copy the clauses you identified in question 1 into the boxes below
   to show whether they are main clauses or subordinate clauses.

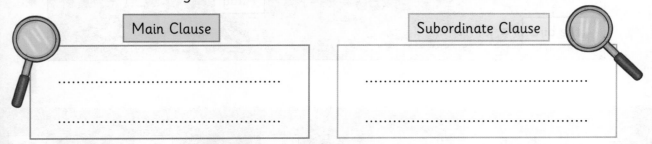

Main Clause   Subordinate Clause

....

....

3. Draw lines to match each main clause to the right subordinate clause.

My sister climbed the tree   when Nura scored a goal.

The whole crowd cheered   because he missed his owner.

The dog was barking   even though she hates heights.

4. Underline the subordinate clause in each sentence below.

Mosi doesn't want to play cards because he prefers chess.

When it is sunny, I play outside with my friends.

We can eat our lunch after we climb up the hill.

Because it was raining heavily, they stayed inside.

5. Use the words in the box to write a sentence.
   Make sure it has a main clause and a subordinate clause.

| teacher | after |
| competition |

....

....

An Extra Challenge

Oops! Terry dropped some subordinate clauses and now they are all jumbled up.
Unscramble the subordinate clauses, then write a main clause to go with each one.

| wanted | the | because | tiny | he | object | to see |

| was | difficult | it | test | although | a |

| important | she | experiment | if | completed | the |

Have you mastered the science
of clauses? Give yourself a tick.

23

Conjunctions

How It Works

Conjunctions are words or phrases that join two parts of a sentence together.

Co-ordinating conjunctions join two main clauses together.

I put my coat on and I went outside.

first main clause co-ordinating conjunction second main clause

These words are all co-ordinating conjunctions:

For And Nor But Or Yet So

Subordinating conjunctions join a subordinate clause to a main clause.

Winter is my favourite season (because) I love snow.

main clause subordinating conjunction subordinate clause

Now Try These

1. Join each pair of sentences together using one of the conjunctions on the right. Use each conjunction once.

   It is cold. I have made some hot chocolate.

   ....

   ....

   Sunil likes rabbits. He likes hamsters.

   ....

   Jo's good at skiing. She has never tried skating.

   ....

   We can go home. We can sleep over.

   ....

or but so and

24

2. Circle the right conjunction to complete each sentence.

School has been cancelled **because** / **although** it is snowing.

Unless / **After** we watched the match, we went home.

I'll stay awake **until** / **before** Mum gets back from work.

3. Underline the conjunction in each sentence below.
   Circle the sentences that use subordinating conjunctions.

I really enjoy running, even though it is hard.

The snowman dances when nobody is watching.

Santa had eaten several mince pies, yet he was still hungry.

Let's make snow angels once we've done our homework.

Should we go sledging or should we stay inside?

An Extra Challenge

Use the conjunctions on the right to join together the clauses in the picture.
How many different sentences can you make?

it was snowing

I went inside

she went snowboarding

it was too cold

he built a snowman

I wanted to play in the snow

Co-ordinating conjunctions:

but   so   and

Subordinating conjunctions:

because   while   when

Are you feeling ice-cool about conjunctions? Tick a box.

Apostrophes

Apostrophes are used to join two words together.
They show where letters have been missed out.

you are = you're   will not = won't

Apostrophes are also used to show who things belong to.
You usually add an apostrophe and an 's' to show possession.

the boy's kit   James's shoe

If a plural noun ends in 's', you only
add an apostrophe to show possession.

the boys' kit ⟵ This means that the kit belongs to more than one boy.

Now Try These

1. Use an apostrophe to shorten each of the phrases below.

she has

....

we are

....

that had

....

were not

....

we would

....

is not

....

what is

....

he will

....

26

2. Complete these sentences by writing out
   the word in the box to show possession.

   Anil ⟶ We went to .... house to watch a film.

   children ⟶ The .... team plays every Tuesday.

   Jess ⟶ It's .... turn to do the washing up today.

   country ⟶ She is the .... best footballer.

   elves ⟶ Everyone loved eating the .... cakes.

3. Add an apostrophe to each word in bold to show possession.

   The **p h o n e s** screen broke when I dropped it on the floor.

   We found the stolen crisps in the **t h i e v e s** pockets.

   Julie painted the picture with a **f r i e n d s** paintbrush.

   The **l o r r i e s** loads were all delivered just in time.

   Bowling is my youngest **b r o t h e r s** favourite hobby.

An Extra Challenge

Can you match the people below to the objects they need for their hobbies?
Using apostrophes for possession, write down who owns each object, e.g. Ana's bike.

Lewis enjoys photography.

My family like playing.

My cousins love skiing.

Carly likes reading.

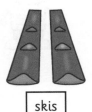
skis

camera

books

cards

How did it go? Are apostrophes your new favourite hobby?

27

Direct speech

How It Works

Inverted commas (or speech marks) go around the actual words that someone says. This is called direct speech. Direct speech always ends with a punctuation mark inside the inverted commas.

If the sentence carries on after the speech, put a comma.

"Hello," said the robot.

comma

If the sentence ends when the speech ends, use a full stop. You also need a comma before the speech starts.

Zoe said, "This robot is awesome."

comma   Direct speech always starts with a capital letter.   full stop

Direct speech can also end with a question mark or an exclamation mark.

Ed said, "Where's my robot?"   "Come back!" he yelled.

Now Try These

1. Write out what each character is saying as direct speech. You'll need to use inverted commas, capital letters and the correct punctuation.

what a great plan that is

.... said Aidan.

what's your name

TR46 asked, ...

I am a special dancing robot

.... said DanC3R.

2. Tick the sentences that use direct speech correctly.

"I can't wait to go to school! squealed Colin." ☐

Amara said, "My favourite food is spaghetti." ☐

Lauren muttered "it's unfair — she always wins." ☐

"I wish I had a robot dog," said Hugh dreamily. ☐

3. On the lines below, rewrite the incorrect sentences from question 2, correcting the mistakes.

....

....

4. The sentences below use direct speech. Can you add the missing punctuation?

Malik shouted This is the best day of my entire life

Why is the robot looking at me like that whispered Tina

The robot inventor said I think there is a big problem

An Extra Challenge

What do you think the characters in the pictures below are saying? Can you write a sentence of direct speech for each character? Don't forget to use inverted commas.

Talia

Jeff

Zac

Tim

Wanda

"Are you a well-oiled machine when it comes to direct speech?"

 ☐   ☐   ☐

Prefixes

How It Works

A prefix is a letter or group of letters that you add to the beginning of a word to form a new word.

dis ➕ agree ➡ disagree

prefix   root word   new word

Prefixes don't change the spelling of the root word.

Now Try These

1. Draw lines to match each prefix to the right root word.
   Write the completed words in the box.

dis

behave

belief

spelt

mis

appear

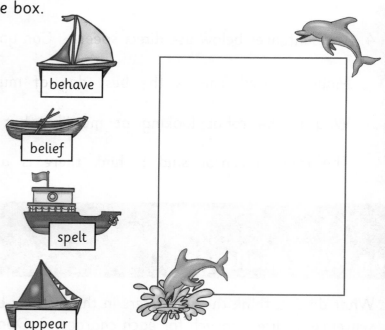

2. Circle the right spelling of each word to complete the sentences.

   Ana accidentally **superglued / subglued** her hand to the table.

   Sonia searched the **transnet / internet** for information.

   The doctor gave me **autobiotics / antibiotics** when I was ill.

   Everyone cheered when the **substar / superstar** stepped onto the stage.

3. Use the prefixes in the box to complete the sentences below.

| in | il | im | ir |

It should be .... legal to talk while I'm watching TV!

It is very .... responsible to play with matches.

Raj complained that the maths test was .... possible.

Swimming without kicking your legs is .... effective.

4. Make three words using the prefixes and root words in the boxes below. For each new word, write a sentence that uses it.

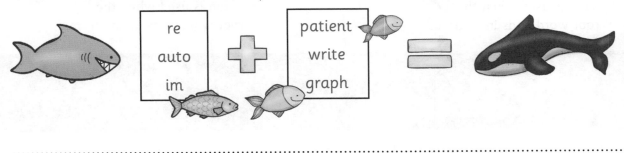

re
auto
im

+

patient
write
graph

=

....

....

....

An Extra Challenge

Here are some prefixes and some root words you can add them to. What do you think each prefix means? Use a dictionary to find more words that start with each prefix.

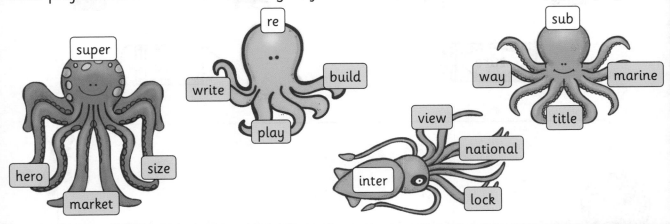

Word endings

How It Works

Some word endings sound similar, but are spelt differently.

For example, the 'shun' sound can be spelt in different ways.

invention   **divi**sion

-tion is usually used when the root word ends in 't' or 'te'.

-sion is used when the root word ends in 'd', 'de' or 'se'.

musician   **discu**ssion

-cian is used when the root word ends in 'c' or 'cs'.

-ssion is used when the root word ends in 'ss' or 'mit'.

Now Try These

1. Draw lines from each word beginning to the right word ending.
   Then, write the words you've made in the box below.

 mea

 na

 adven

trea

 furni

 pres

 crea

pic

 -ture

 -sure

2. Circle the words below that are spelt wrong.
   Can you write them on the lines without any mistakes?

   expretion   optician
   mention   television

   relasion   confution

   creassion   reduction

   ....

   ....

   ....

   ....

3. Should the words below end in **able** or **ible**? Add the right ending to each one.

   break ✚ .... ➡ ....

   avail ✚ .... ➡ ....

   poss ✚ .... ➡ ....

   terr ✚ .... ➡ ....

   prob ✚ .... ➡ ....

An Extra Challenge

Oh dear! Jeni's dog has eaten some of the word endings from her homework
and she needs your help to replace them. Can you rewrite the sentences
below, adding the right word endings so that Jeni's homework make sense?

When I have lei..... time, I like to read
litera..... . I think it's incred..... that
libraries make books access..... for free
— you don't need permi..... or an
invita.....! My favourite book is about
a magi..... — it's very read..... .

How did it go? Was this page
an occasion for celebration?

Tricky words

How It Works

There's no getting around it, some words are tricky to spell.

lamb

Some words contain silent letters that you can't hear when you say the word out loud.

they

Some contain sounds that aren't spelt as you would expect. In 'they' the 'ay' sound is spelt 'ey'.

caffeine

Some words don't follow spelling rules. 'Caffeine' breaks the 'i' before 'e' rule.

Now Try These

1. Circle the words below that are spelt wrong.
   Can you write them in the box without any mistakes?

animul

parachute

famly

environment

camouflage

memrable

experience

interesting

natral   desend   curious   peeple   daughter   speshial

2. The words below are all missing a silent letter.
   Fill in the missing letters to complete the words.

....nome   si....n   cou....d   c....emist   ans....er

w....ale   r....yme   ....nock   w....at   rei....n

3. Circle the right spelling of each word to complete the sentences below.

The safari **veicle / vehicle** was decorated with zebra stripes.

February / Febuary is my favourite month.

"It's absolute **kaos / chaos** !" exclaimed Fran.

My mum runs her own **bisiness / business**.

4. The 'ay' sound can be spelt **ai**, **ey** or **eigh**. Choose the right spelling of the 'ay' sound to complete each word below.

African elephants can w............... up to six tonnes.

When I'm older, I'll go to school on the tr...............n.

My little brother is five years old and I am ....t.

You should ob............... the school rules.

5. Write each of the words below in a sentence.

science ➡ ....

difference ➡ ....

An Extra Challenge

Can you solve the clues to complete this crossword of tricky words?

Down

1. A place where you can borrow books.
2. Another word for middle.
4. Something you do to clear your throat.

Across

3. Another word for strange.
5. Another word for certain.
6. Birds are covered in these.

How did it go? Did you find this page tricky?

35

Answers

Pages 2-3 — Word types

1. noun: kennel, bird; adjective: shaggy, naughty; verb: barked; adverb: angrily

2. Any sensible sentence, e.g. The naughty dog barked angrily at the bird.

3. Sophie <u>absolutely</u> <u>loves</u> reading <u>books</u> about <u>friendly</u>

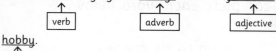

animals.
Dominic <u>said</u> singing has <u>always</u> been his <u>favourite</u>

| verb | | adverb | | adjective |

<u>hobby</u>.

noun

4. Millie doesn't <u>often</u> tidy her bedroom. — adverb
He normally <u>walks</u> back home after school. — verb
The <u>shark</u> showed off its glistening teeth. — noun
Sadiq said that the film was <u>amazing</u>. — adjective

An Extra Challenge

E.g. run, jog, fish, jump, leap, hug, drink, kick

Pages 4-5 — Verbs

1. Correct: He fed his parrot a peanut. / Last week, I went to a pirate feast. / You clean the ship with your mop. / We eat sea biscuits for lunch.
Incorrect: The pirates counts their treasure. / She love exploring desert islands. / I has to walk the plank. / Yesterday, he says hello to the captain.

2. Yesterday, it <u>was</u> raining so my dad <u>drove</u> me to school. After school finished, I <u>went</u> to the park. I ran around and <u>played</u> on the swings until my mum <u>picked</u> me up.

3. I <u>is</u> angry with the other pirates. — am
We <u>goes</u> to the treasure island. — go
Lara <u>feel</u> very seasick. — feels
They <u>shouts</u> really loudly. — shout

An Extra Challenge

Any sensible description, e.g. <u>I swam</u> to the island and then <u>I ran</u> along the beach. <u>I saw</u> a good place to hide the treasure and <u>I dug</u> a hole.

Pages 6-7 — Verbs with 'ing'

1. She is running. / I was smiling. / They are playing. / We were jumping. / You were speaking. / It is raining.

2. Present Progressive: She is running. / They are playing. / It is raining.
Past Progressive: I was smiling. / We were jumping. / You were speaking.

3. Jeremy <u>was putting</u> pink frosting on his cupcakes.
They <u>were making</u> brownies for the bake sale.
Hiba <u>was cutting</u> her birthday cake into slices.
We <u>were cleaning</u> the kitchen when my uncle arrived.

I <u>was feeling</u> happy because my sister had made me a biscuit.
It was a disaster — the icing <u>was sliding</u> off the cake!

4. You were laughing. / I am skipping. / They are painting. / Ash was singing. / We are playing.

An Extra Challenge

Any sensible description, e.g. Chidi was eating a biscuit. Ellen was stirring the mixture. Marta was icing a cake. You would use the present progressive form if the children were doing the baking right now. E.g. Chidi is eating a biscuit. Ellen is stirring the mixture. Marta is icing a cake.

Pages 8-9 — Verbs with 'have'

1. Present Perfect Form: He has gone out. / You have said hello. / We have begun dancing. / They have swum for hours.
Past Perfect Form: She had smiled kindly. / I had hidden the chair. / We had cooked dinner. / It had torn my coat.

2. Rhys has <u>rung</u> the bell very loudly. — present perfect
It was so cold that the lake had <u>frozen</u>. — past perfect
My friends had <u>come</u> to stay with us. — past perfect
Someone has <u>stolen</u> the dinosaur tooth.
— present perfect

3. I <u>have learned</u> about fossils at school. I <u>have decided</u> to go to the museum to learn more and I <u>have invited</u> Lila to come too.

An Extra Challenge

E.g. to draw — drew / have drawn; to write — wrote / have written; to ride — rode / have ridden; to sing — sang / have sung; to give — gave / have given; to fall — fell / have fallen; to eat — ate / have eaten

Pages 10-11 — Pronouns

1. hers, mine, them, her, it, ours

2. hers, mine, ours

3. Clare enjoys playing the drums and <u>she</u> plays <u>them</u> well. Grant and Salem hate maths because <u>they</u> think <u>it</u> is boring.

4. You can't wear those socks because they're <u>mine</u>.
My cat dislikes water — <u>it</u> hates getting wet.
Nadia and I were noisy, so the teacher told <u>us</u> off.
It was my brother's birthday, so I gave <u>him</u> a gift.

An Extra Challenge

a. his; b. theirs; c. hers; d. hers; e. his

Pages 12-13 — Determiners

1. We are <u>a</u> team of <u>four</u> penguin heroes. We use <u>our</u> superpowers for good.
<u>Most</u> people would be surprised to learn that <u>every</u> penguin has <u>a</u> superpower.

Answers

My superpower is sliding on <u>my</u> stomach at supersonic speeds — I've used <u>this</u> power to catch <u>many</u> baddies! <u>Some</u> penguins use <u>their</u> powers for evil deeds, like stealing fish fingers from <u>the</u> supermarket — it's <u>our</u> job to stop them.

2. one, This, Several, Most

3. If I had <u>a</u> superpower, it would be <u>the</u> power of flight.
    Zack and <u>his</u> sidekick defeated <u>six</u> bad guys.
    There was <u>an</u> explosion, but luckily nobody was hurt.

An Extra Challenge

Any sensible determiners, e.g. <u>Several</u> superheroes used <u>their</u> powers to try to defeat <u>this</u> baddie.
Dr Dastardly is <u>an</u> evil genius.
<u>Some</u> determiners were found with <u>the</u> help of <u>those</u> brave heroes.
<u>That</u> wicked super-villain imprisoned <u>lots of</u> people but <u>one</u> prisoner escaped.

Pages 14-15 — Prepositions

1. after, beside, until, between

2. The witch finally found her hat <u>after</u> a long search.
    Mai couldn't choose <u>between</u> the pizza and the burger.
    "We have <u>until</u> sunset to cast the spell," whispered Nigel.
    Honey promised to stay <u>beside</u> me, but she ran away.

3. inside — where; during — when; at — when; on — where; due to — why

4. Any sensible answers, e.g.
    Romesh put his cloak <u>on the coat rack</u>.
    They went for a walk <u>in the afternoon</u>.
    Lisa was running <u>along the pavement</u>.

An Extra Challenge

Any sensible sentences, e.g. The skeleton is <u>on</u> the roof. / The ghost is <u>above</u> the fire. / The witch is <u>next to</u> the cauldron. / The moon is <u>in</u> the sky. / The spider is <u>below</u> the moon. / The pumpkins are <u>beside</u> the witch.

Pages 16-17 — Noun phrases

1. a noble knight / the starry robe / the towering giant

2. unicorn, duck, afternoon

3. Rob likes to cut the grass with <u>his huge red lawnmower</u>.
    Shazia was amazed by <u>the huge castle on top of the hill</u>.
    Sarah wrote <u>a long, boring book about the history of paperclips</u>.

4. Any sensible noun phrases, e.g.
    The prince ate <u>the delicious sandwich from the cafe</u>.
    She ran away from <u>the terrifying monster in the kitchen</u>.
    The queen lives in <u>a grand palace beside a river</u>.

An Extra Challenge

Any sensible noun phrases, e.g. a happy dwarf with a red hat / the old house in the middle of the forest / the big green ogre on the path / a mysterious man in a long black cloak / the friendly wolf with soft, grey fur

Pages 18-19 — Planet hopping

A   True

B   On a <u>tipical</u> day, Millie bakes three delicious chocolate cakes.

C   When <u>the</u> alien's rocket crashed, <u>every</u> star went out.

D   jolly

E   My cat was playing with <u>his</u> toy.

F   The <u>astronaut's</u> found walking on the <u>Moons'</u> surface hard because there <u>wasnt</u> much gravity.

G   False

Pages 20-21 — Adverbials

1. really easily / every weekend / quite regularly / in the trees / while it is sunny

2. The children tend the garden <u>very carefully</u>.
    The hungry chicks followed Pavel <u>into the house</u>.
    He tries to have a healthy lunch <u>every single day</u>.
    <u>Before I went into the garden</u>, I put my wellies on.

3. In the garden, there are lots of colourful flowers.
    After waving frantically, we finally got Jen's attention.
    On special occasions, I have ice cream for breakfast.
    Tomorrow afternoon, we will plant the seeds.

4. In the morning, the frost will melt.
    During the holidays, I visited my aunt.
    When it is scared, the dog barks.

An Extra Challenge

Any sensible sentences that include adverbials, e.g. Brenda is climbing up a tree. / The bird is singing very loudly. / In the garden, Laura is flying her kite. / Andy is planting some seeds in the ground. / Lucy is watering the seeds with her watering can.

Pages 22-23 — Clauses

1. Phrase: the kind teacher / with enthusiasm / in the test tube
    Clause: we love reading / before she spoke / because he did it / I passed the test

2. Main Clause: we love reading / I passed the test
    Subordinate Clause: before she spoke / because he did it

3. My sister climbed the tree even though she hates heights.
    The whole crowd cheered when Nura scored a goal.
    The dog was barking because he missed his owner.

4. Mosi doesn't want to play cards <u>because he prefers chess</u>.
    <u>When it is sunny</u>, I play outside with my friends.
    We can eat our lunch <u>after we climb up the hill</u>.
    <u>Because it was raining heavily</u>, they stayed inside.

5. Any sensible sentence, e.g. <u>After the science competition</u>, the <u>teacher</u> gave the class a prize.

An Extra Challenge

Any sensible sentences, e.g. Shaun peered through the microscope because he wanted to see the tiny object.

Answers

Although it was a difficult test, Sandra got full marks.
If she completed the important experiment, Becca would win a prize.

Pages 24-25 — Conjunctions

1. It is cold <u>so</u> I have made some hot chocolate.
   Sunil likes rabbits <u>and</u> he likes hamsters.
   Jo's good at skiing <u>but</u> she has never tried skating.
   We can go home <u>or</u> we can sleep over.

2. because, After, until

3. I really enjoy running, <u>even though</u> it is hard.
   The snowman dances <u>when</u> nobody is watching.
   Santa had eaten several mince pies, <u>yet</u> he was still hungry.
   Let's make snow angels <u>once</u> we've done our homework.
   Should we go sledging <u>or</u> should we stay inside?
   You should have circled sentences 1, 2 and 4.

An Extra Challenge

Any sensible sentences, e.g. I wanted to play in the snow but it was too cold. / It was too cold so I went inside. / She went snowboarding and he built a snowman. / He built a snowman while it was snowing. / Because it was snowing, he built a snowman. / When she went snowboarding, I went inside.

Pages 26-27 — Apostrophes

1. she's, we're, that'd, weren't, we'd, isn't, what's, he'll

2. Anil's, children's, Jess's, country's, elves'

3. phone<u>'s</u>, thieves<u>'</u>, friend<u>'s</u>, lorries<u>'</u>, brother<u>'s</u>

An Extra Challenge

Lewis's camera / my family's cards / my cousins' skis / Carly's books

Pages 28-29 — Direct speech

1. "What a great plan that is!" said Aidan.
   TR46 asked, "What's your name?"
   "I am a special dancing robot," said DanC3R.

2. Amara said, "My favourite food is spaghetti."
   "I wish I had a robot dog," said Hugh dreamily.

3. "I can't wait to go to school!" squealed Colin.
   Lauren muttered, "It's unfair — she always wins."

4. Malik shouted, "This is the best day of my entire life!"
   "Why is the robot looking at me like that?" whispered Tina.
   The robot inventor said, "I think there is a big problem."

An Extra Challenge

Any sensible sentences, e.g.
Talia screamed, "I'm scared of robots!"
Jeff said, "Don't be afraid."
"Let me help you get up," said Zac.
"Thank you, Zac," said Tim.
"These fireworks are beautiful!" gasped Wanda.

Pages 30-31 — Prefixes

1. disbelief, disappear, misbehave, misspelt

2. superglued, internet, antibiotics, superstar

3. illegal, irresponsible, impossible, ineffective

4. Any sensible sentences, e.g.
   I had to <u>rewrite</u> my work because it was messy.
   The athlete gave me her <u>autograph</u>.
   Harry is very <u>impatient</u>.

An Extra Challenge

super — more than; re — again; inter — between;
sub — under

Pages 32-33 — Word endings

1. nature, adventure, furniture, creature, picture, measure, treasure, pressure

2. The correct spellings are: expre<u>ssion</u>, rela<u>tion</u>, confu<u>sion</u>, crea<u>tion</u>

3. break<u>able</u>, avail<u>able</u>, poss<u>ible</u>, terr<u>ible</u>, prob<u>able</u>

An Extra Challenge

When I have lei<u>sure</u> time, I like to read litera<u>ture</u>. I think it's incred<u>ible</u> that libraries make books access<u>ible</u> for free — you don't need permi<u>ssion</u> or an invita<u>tion</u>! My favourite book is about a magi<u>cian</u> — it's very read<u>able</u>.

Pages 34-35 — Tricky words

1. The correct spellings are: animal, family, natural, descend, people, special, memorable

2. <u>g</u>nome, si<u>g</u>n, coul<u>d</u>, <u>ch</u>emist, ans<u>w</u>er, <u>wh</u>ale, r<u>h</u>yme, <u>k</u>nock, <u>wh</u>at, reign

3. vehicle, February, chaos, business

4. w<u>eigh</u>, tr<u>ai</u>n, <u>eigh</u>t, ob<u>ey</u>

5. Any sensible sentences, e.g.
   My favourite subject is <u>science</u>.
   I can't tell the <u>difference</u> between the twins.

An Extra Challenge

Down: 1. library 2. centre 4. cough
Across: 3. weird 5. sure 6. feathers